THE WHIZZY DIZZY BIKE RIDE

Written by
Elizabeth Dinn Marsh

Illustrated by Patrick Girouard

For my husband Michael
and our children
Nadine, Denver Paige, and Iyla

The triplets were racing their shiny new bikes for just the second time since losing their training wheels.

Sparkly purple for Iyla and Nadine.
Lightning white for Denver Paige.

The girls raced around and around the circle at a whizzy, dizzy pace, only slowing down to pass each other or turn.

The sisters still needed help to start pedaling, but if they fell, they got back on their bikes in a flash!

When Denver Paige rode too close to
Iyla their bikes wibbled and wobbled.

Then Denver Paige wibbled and Iyla wobbled, and Iyla flew off her bike and onto the grass!

Iyla was mangled and tangled in her bike.
Her mom sprinted toward her.

Iyla was rattled from the fall. There was no blood, not even a scratch, but she held her arm close.

Denver Paige had also fallen, but she got up quickly to check on Iyla. Nadine dashed toward Iyla too.

Through her tears, Iyla said she didn't want to ride anymore, but her sisters begged for one more circle around.

When Denver Paige and Nadine were done, their mom packed up the bikes and drove the tired girls home.

Iyla didn't say a word during the drive home.

While making dinner, their mom noticed that Iyla was not her usual bouncy, happy self. She guarded her arm closely.

After dinner, they went to see the doctor. Iyla
was very brave during her x-ray. The image
showed a fracture near her elbow.

Iyla chose a bright red cast. It was soon covered with messages of love from her sisters. Her mom even sprinkled it with sparkly glitter!

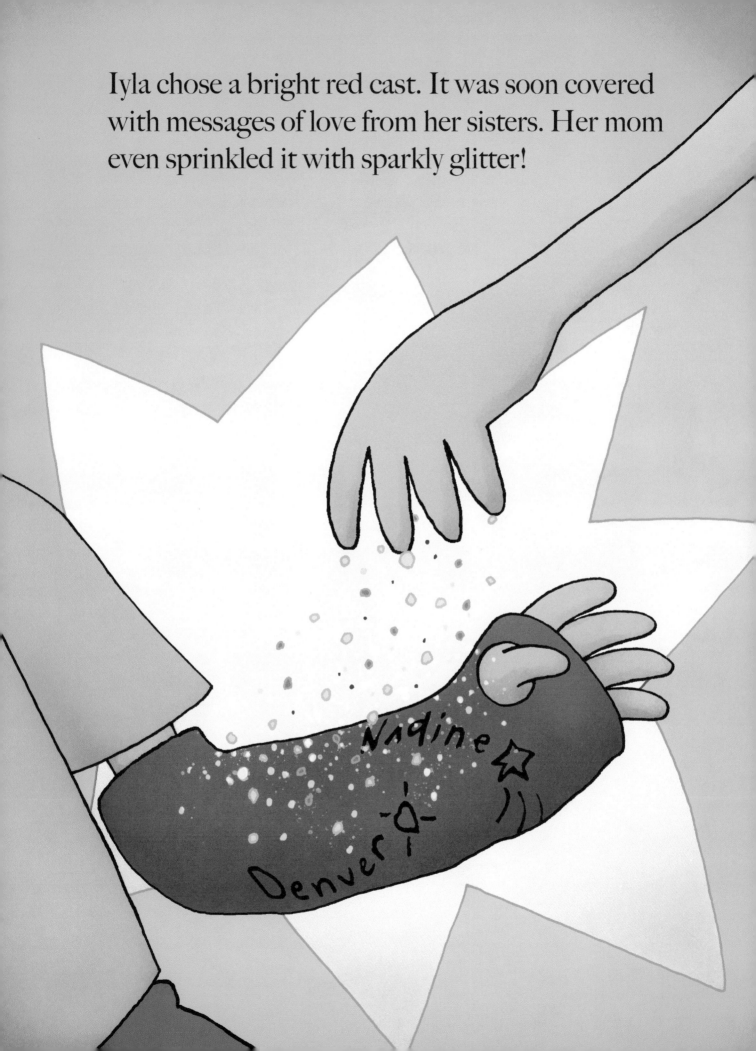

The cast had become a beautiful work of art, and Iyla was proud to show it to her kindergarten class!

Many weeks passed, and eventually the fracture healed. But when the cast came off, Iyla did NOT want to ride her bike. Nadine and Denver Paige tried to encourage her, but the memory of her crash was still too fresh.

During winter break, their friends Avery and Sophia asked the triplets to go on a bike riding playdate. Their mom was overjoyed about the girls riding their bikes again! Would Iyla ride? She dusted the bikes and checked their tires. She packed three bikes and three helmets into their car.

Denver Paige and Nadine were delighted, but Iyla was silent. She was worried about getting hurt again.

Iyla practiced riding with her mom close by. She wibbled and wobbled, trying to keep her balance. Iyla fell, got back up and bravely tried again. She fell once more.

Iyla's sisters, Avery, and Sophia yelled for her
to join them on the track.

Iyla did it! She was steady and ready! Soon she was tearing around the track at a whizzy, dizzy pace.

She squealed in delight as she whipped around corners or passed the other girls.

Although it had taken a while, Iyla had gotten on the bike. She wasn't going to let one accident stop her from enjoying herself.

Her sisters and friends cheered her on as they all rode in circles at a whizzy, dizzy pace.

Iyla learned a lesson and loves riding her bike!

CPSIA information can be obtained at www.ICGtesting.com
Printed in the USA
BVIW120205271020
591910BV00012B/79